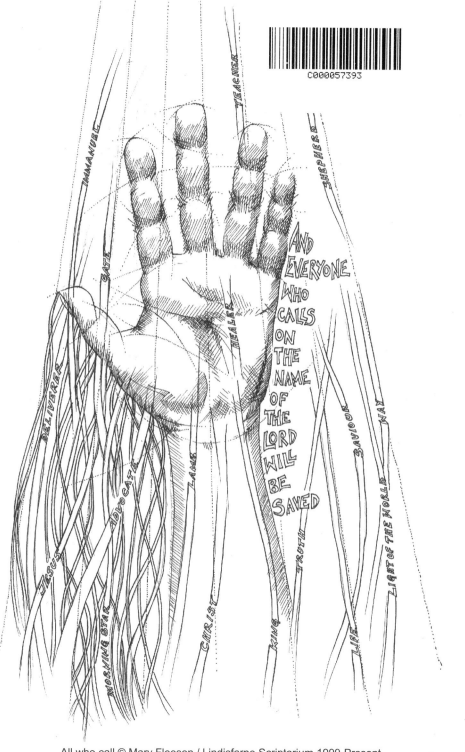

We saw his star in the east and have come to worship him ... Herod called the Magi secretly and found out from them the exact time the star had appeared... and the star they had seen in the east went ahead of them until it stopped over the place where the child was ... When they saw the star they were overjoyed... The sun has one kind of splendour, the moon another, and the stars another, and star differs from star in splendour. So will it be with the resurrection of the dead. The body that is sown is perishable, it is raised imperishable, it is sown in dishonour, it is raised in glory; it is sown in weakness, it is raised in power; it is sown a natural body, it is raised a spiritual body

PRAISE TO YOU LORD JESUS CHRIST KING OF ENDLESS GLORY

Praise to You © Mary Fleeson / Lindisfarne Scriptorium 1999-Present

I HAVE SET MY RAINBOW IN THE CLOUDS AND IT WILL BE THE SIGN OF THE COVENANT BETWEEN ME AND THE EARTH

David's Praise © Mary Fleeson / Lindisfarne Scriptorium 1999-Present

"No eye has seen, no ear has heard, no mind has conceived what God has prepared for those who love him"

tell you that in the same way there will be more rejoicing in heaven over one sinner who repents than over ninety-nine righteous persons who do not need to repent

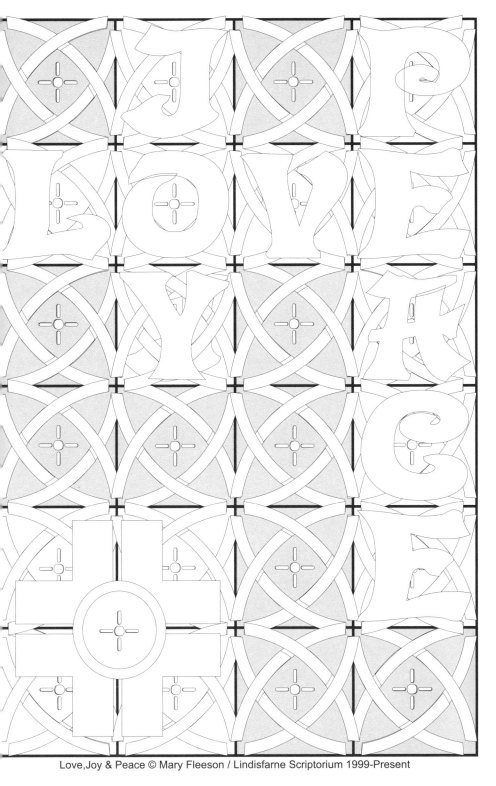

Love,Joy & Peace © Mary Fleeson / Lindisfarne Scriptorium 1999-Present

Peace I leave with you; my peace I give you.

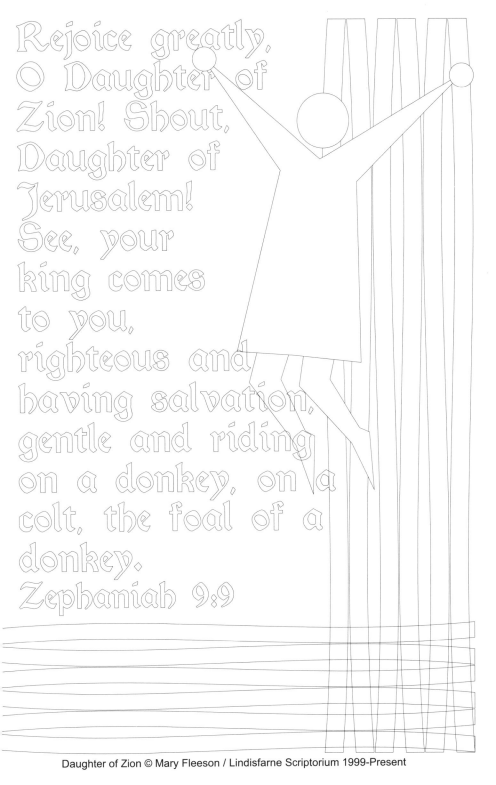

Rejoice greatly, O Daughter of Zion! Shout, Daughter of Jerusalem! See, your king comes to you, righteous and having salvation, gentle and riding on a donkey, on a colt, the foal of a donkey. Zephaniah 9:9

Daughter of Zion © Mary Fleeson / Lindisfarne Scriptorium 1999-Present